INTRODUCTION

Welcome To Fishing And Our Environment

If you want to go fishing, it's easy. Just look around you. There's water everywhere, whether you live in a big city on the coast or on a farm in the country. No wonder fishing is such a popular activity. Anybody can fish if they want to.

Just as when you play games, the more you fish, the better you become. Each time you go fishing, you learn more about it. You will also learn other important things, if you pay attention to what's going on in the water around you. You will see that many creatures besides fish live in the water, and depend on it to live. And other creatures live at the water's edge, or come to it to feed and drink. Everything, especially people, must have clean water. People who like to fish a lot learn that lesson quicker than most, and understand it better.

We want you to think about that every time you go fishing. We hope that this book will help remind you. Always remember how important the water is to all living things, and how we all must help keep it clean.

Dedicated In Fond Memory To
Carl "Sully" Sullivan
(1926-1991)
Executive Director Of The American Fisheries Society
A Tireless Fisheries Leader, Friend And Servant.
Sully Enjoyed To The Fullest His Every Opportunity
To Fish With His Own Children And Grandchildren.
He Loved Young People And Labored To The Very End
To Ensure Their Fishing Tomorrows.

Tacklebox Checklist

Before you go fishing, make sure you have at least the following:

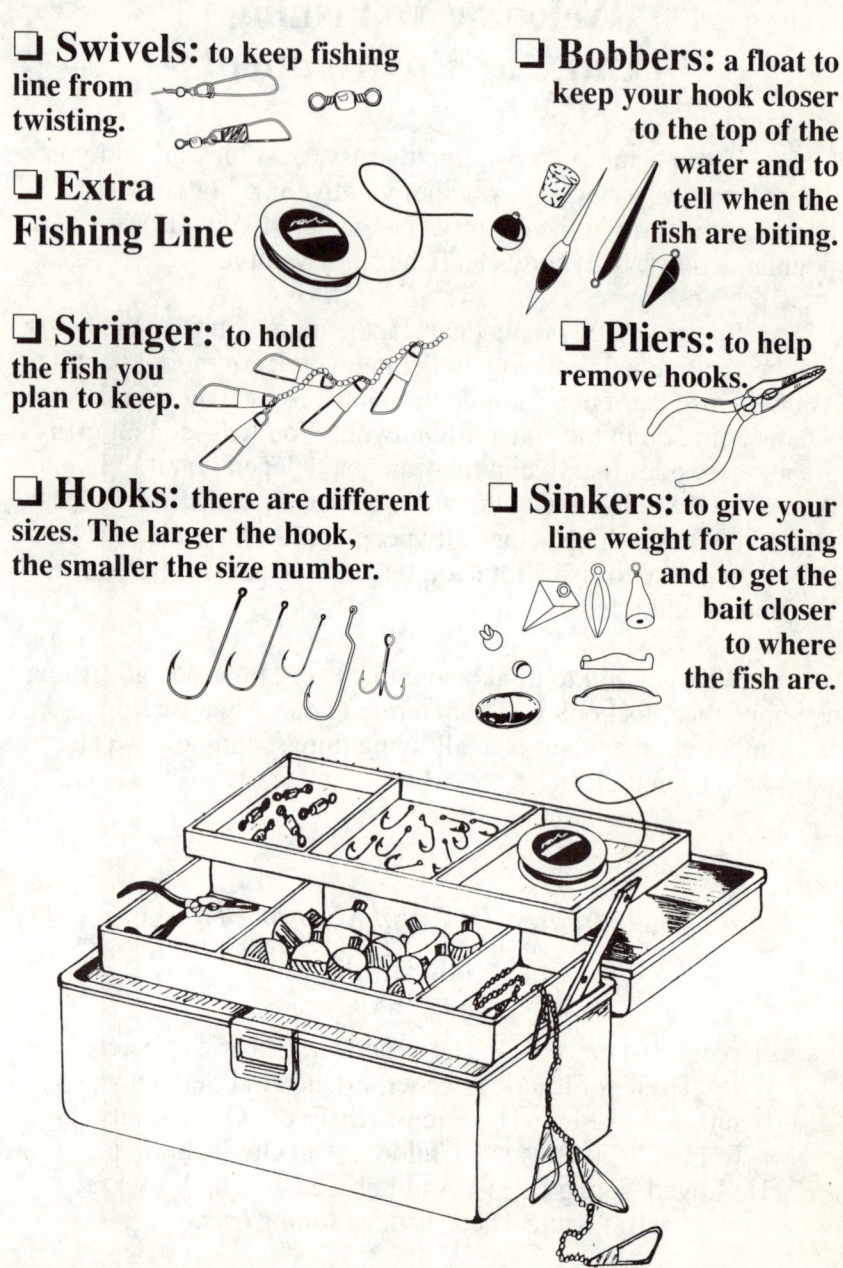

- **Swivels:** to keep fishing line from twisting.

- **Extra Fishing Line**

- **Stringer:** to hold the fish you plan to keep.

- **Hooks:** there are different sizes. The larger the hook, the smaller the size number.

- **Bobbers:** a float to keep your hook closer to the top of the water and to tell when the fish are biting.

- **Pliers:** to help remove hooks.

- **Sinkers:** to give your line weight for casting and to get the bait closer to where the fish are.

Important Items For Boating Safety

Fishing and boating can be fun, but remember safety comes first. Decode the following secret words to see what you should take with you when you go near the water.

__ __ __ __   __ __ __ __ __ __
23 7   3   1   19 2   6   16 1   17

  __ __ __ __ __ __ __ __ __
  18 24 9   18 6   22 1   1   9

__ __ __ __ __ __ __ __ __
18 24 9   5   23 2   18 18 1   18

        __ __ __ __ __ __
        7   9   18 1   6   17

__ __ __ __ __ __ __ __
22 1   15 1   23 23 1   9   17

        __ __ __ __ __
        3   7   22 18 17

    __ __ __ __ __ __
    2   7   8   16 7   17

            __ __ __
            11 2   17

        __ __ __ __ __ __
        3   22 7   1   9   8

SECRET DECODER KEY

a=2 b=4 c=6 d=8 e=1 f=3 g=5 h=11 i=7 j=19 k=16 l=23 m=13 n=9 o=20 p=15 q=10 r=22 s=18 t=17 u=24 v=12 w=26 x=21 y=25 z=14

Answers: Life Jacket, Sunscreen, Sunglasses, Insect Repellent, First Aid Kit, Hat, Friend

Designer Rod

This rod needs gear!

Put together equipment for your favorite kind of fishing by using the pictures below. Choose your favorite reel, bobber or sinker and lure or hook, and draw it where it belongs on the rod. If you want, you can just draw a line from each piece of equipment to where it belongs on the rod.

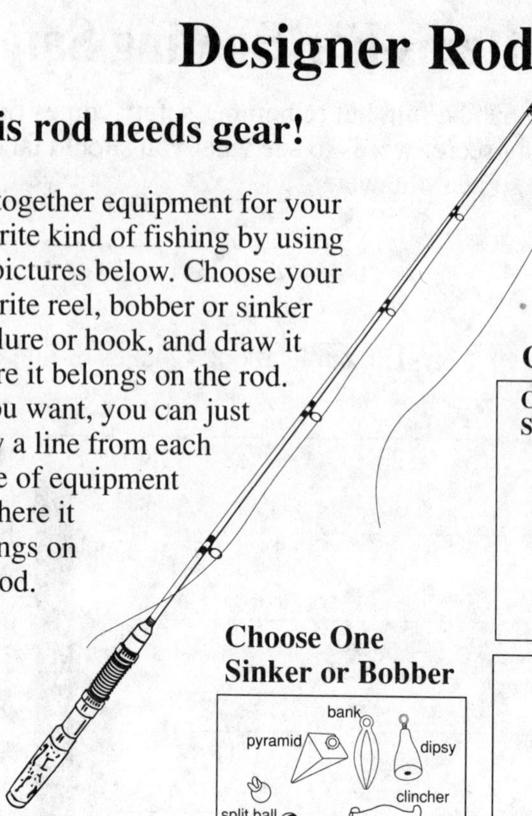

Choose One Reel:

Closed-Face Spinning Reel

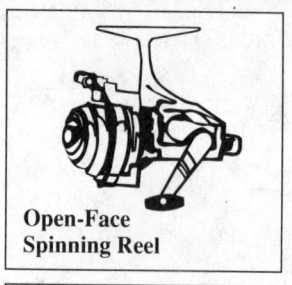

Open-Face Spinning Reel

Fly Fishing Reel

Baitcasting Reel

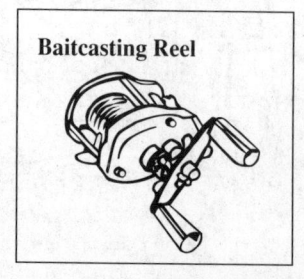

Choose One Sinker or Bobber

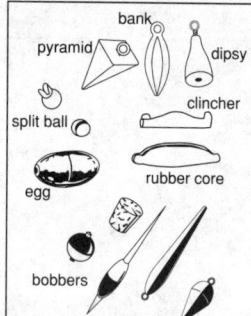

bank
pyramid
dipsy
split ball
clincher
egg
rubber core
bobbers

Choose One Swivel

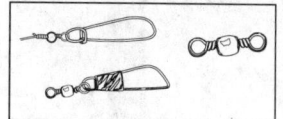

Choose One Lure or Hook:

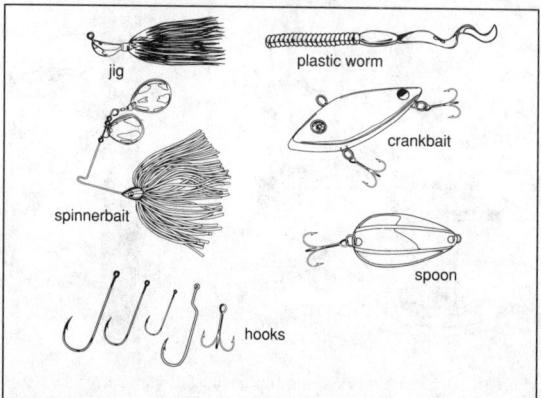

jig
plastic worm
crankbait
spinnerbait
spoon
hooks

A Good Fishing Knot

A regular knot will come untied on your nylon fishing line and the wrong kind of knot will cause your line to break too easily. This knot will keep your hook on the line. This is called a **Palomar Knot.**

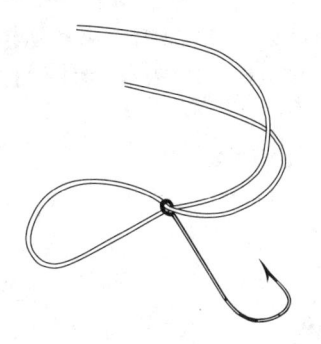

1. Double about 4 inches of line and pass loop through eye.

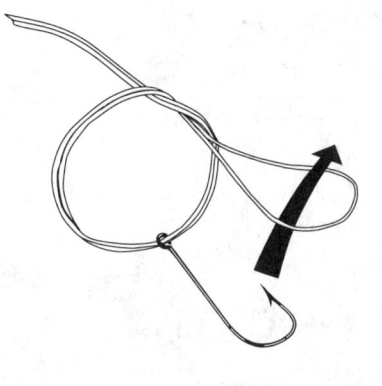

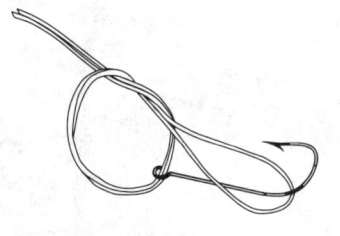

2. Let hook hang loose and tie overhand knot in doubled line.

3. Pull loop of line far enough to pass over hook, swivel, or lure.

4. Pull tag end and standing line to tighten. Moisten before tightening. Clip tag end.

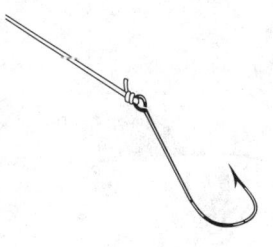

Water As An Environment

Fish enjoy living in a clean and healthy environment, just as people do. Fish will live well in areas where there is lots of food, clean water, and cover like trees, stumps, grass and rocks. Fish do not live well in polluted waters.

Circle 10 things wrong with this environment.

How To Bait Your Hook With Live Bait

Can you name the types of bait being used?

Choose from the names below: Draw a line from the bait to its name.

Crawfish

Minnow

Earthworm

Grasshopper

Frog

Grubworm

Cricket

An A-*MAZE*-ing Fish!
TRY YOUR HAND AT THIS TRICKY MAZE.
DON'T LET THIS BIG ONE GET AWAY!

START HERE!

Microscopic Water World

Many tiny plants and animals live in the water. They only can be seen with a microscope or magnifying glass. These small forms of life are important food to many fish and insects.

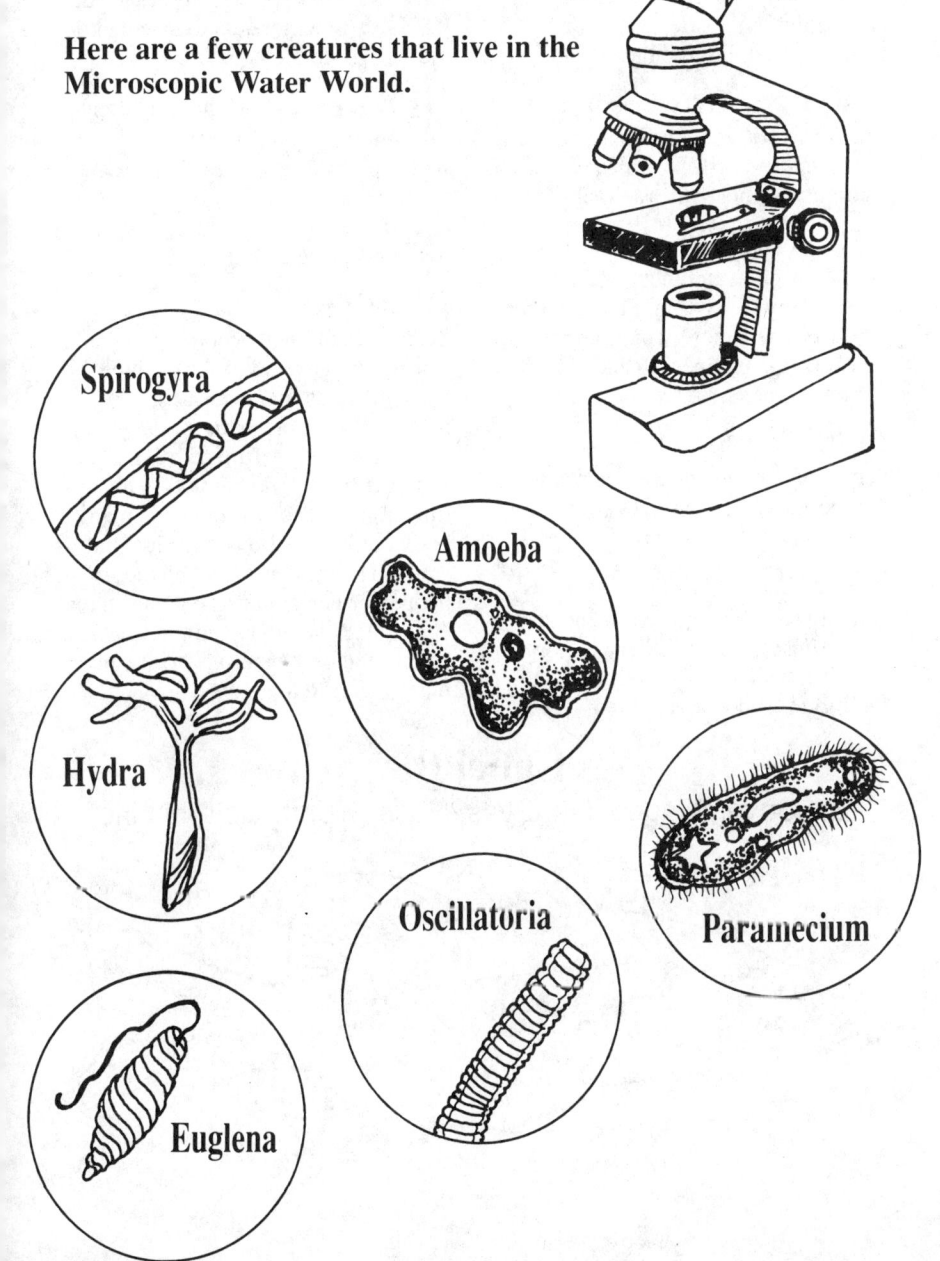

Here are a few creatures that live in the Microscopic Water World.

Spirogyra

Amoeba

Hydra

Paramecium

Oscillatoria

Euglena

How Do Fish...

SWIM? . . . Fish swim by flexing their bodies and tail (caudal fin) back and forth. This is done by expanding their muscles on one side of their body, while relaxing the muscles on the other side, propelling them forward through the water.

EAT? . . . Fish eat mostly other smaller water creatures including small fish and insects. A fish eats with its mouth as most other animal life.

BREATHE? . . . Fish breathe with their gills, and they need a constant supply of oxygen. They get oxygen from the water by pumping it past the gills by opening and closing their gill covers.

SEE? . . . The eyes of a fish are very similar to human eyes, and a fish sees best at close range. However, most fish cannot see directly behind them.

SMELL? . . . A fish's nose is actually two openings on the head. Their sense of smell is very important to a fish, because it helps them find their food, and warns them of danger.

TASTE? . . . Fish have taste buds, just like humans. Fish taste buds have the ability to distinguish the difference between sweet, sour, salty and bitter. Taste buds are inside the fish's mouth, on its tongue and on the outside of the body.

HEAR? . . . Fish have a lateral line along each side of their body which picks up pressure changes and vibrating sounds in the water. The lateral line helps a fish find and capture food and avoid enemies.

REPRODUCE? . . . Reproduction is different according to the species but generally follows three basic methods. In most cases, the female drops eggs in the water which are immediately fertilized by sperm from the male. Another way is for fertilization to occur within the females body before she drops them into the water. The third and final method happens when the female retains the eggs within her body and the young are born alive. Some sharks and guppies give birth this way.

Label the
Gill Cover, Caudal Fin, Eyes, Nose, Mouth, Lateral Line

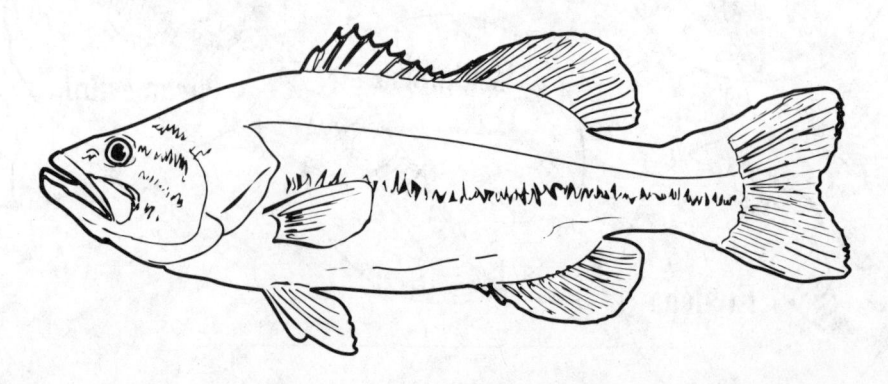

Water Home

Connect the dots to finish the picture.

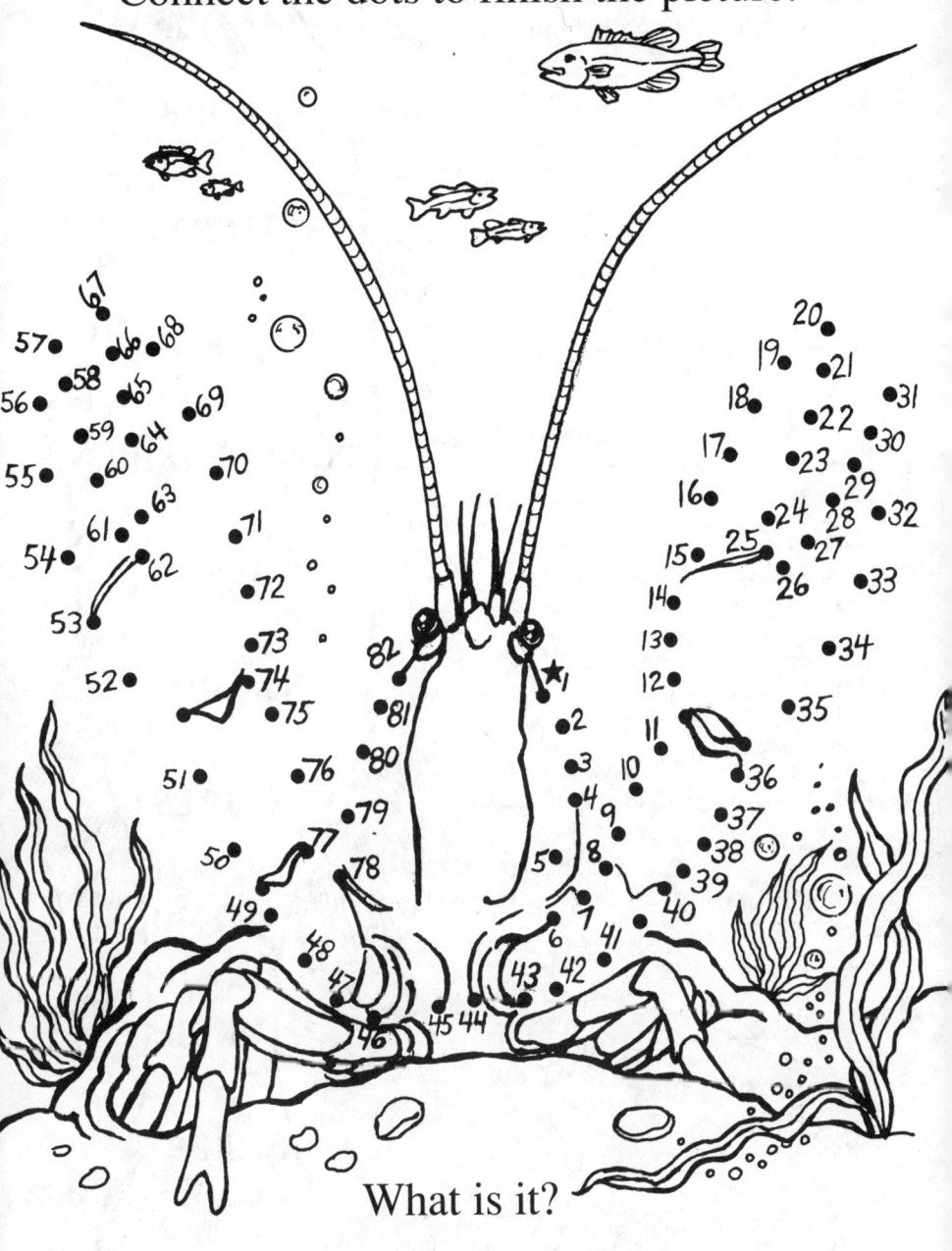

What is it?

____ ____ ____

Scrambled Fishing Items

Unscramble the letters to find out what items are used to go fishing.

1. _ _ _ _ _ _

2. _ _ _ _ _ _ _ _

3. _ _ _ _ _ _ _ _

4. _ _ _ _ _ _ _ _ _ _ _

5. _ _ _ _ _ _ _

6. _ _ _ _ _ _ _

7. _ _ _ _ _ _

8. _ _ _ _ _

9. _ _ _ _

10. _ _ _ _

BREOBB

RGITSRNE

WCHSRIFA

PSOSRAPGEHR

NRIPENS

NWIMON

KNIRES

RWSMO

OKOH

EREL

Answers: 1. BOBBER 2. STRINGER 3. CRAWFISH 4. GRASSHOPPER 5. SPINNER 6. MINNOW 7. SINKER 8. WORMS 9. HOOK 10. REEL

Pick-N-Choose

The black boxes below are types of signs you may see when you go camping, fishing or swimming.

Can you figure out what they mean?

Circle the signs that you would find near the water.

Put an **X** on the signs that represent the activities you like to do.

Living Waters

RIVER

BAY

MARSH

MAN[grove]

DUNES

BEACH

BA[Y]

NEARSHORE

OFFSHORE

Regardless of where you live, the water in the river that flows near you ultimately runs into the sea. On the way, the water provides nourishment for many types of plants, fish and animals. These living things may depend on different kinds of habitat, but one thing stays the same — all need clean water to survive.

Fishing for Facts!

Fish are important to us. They provide food for millions of people and fishermen enjoy catching them for sport.

Fish are also important in the balance of nature. They eat plants and animals and, in turn, become food for plants and animals. This is called a food chain.

The balance of plants and animals in a lake may be upset by people catching too many fish of one kind. This is why limits are set on the number of fish you may keep. Remember, it is necessary for you to learn the fishing rules for your lake. You must take only the legal size and number of fish in order to help keep your lake healthy.

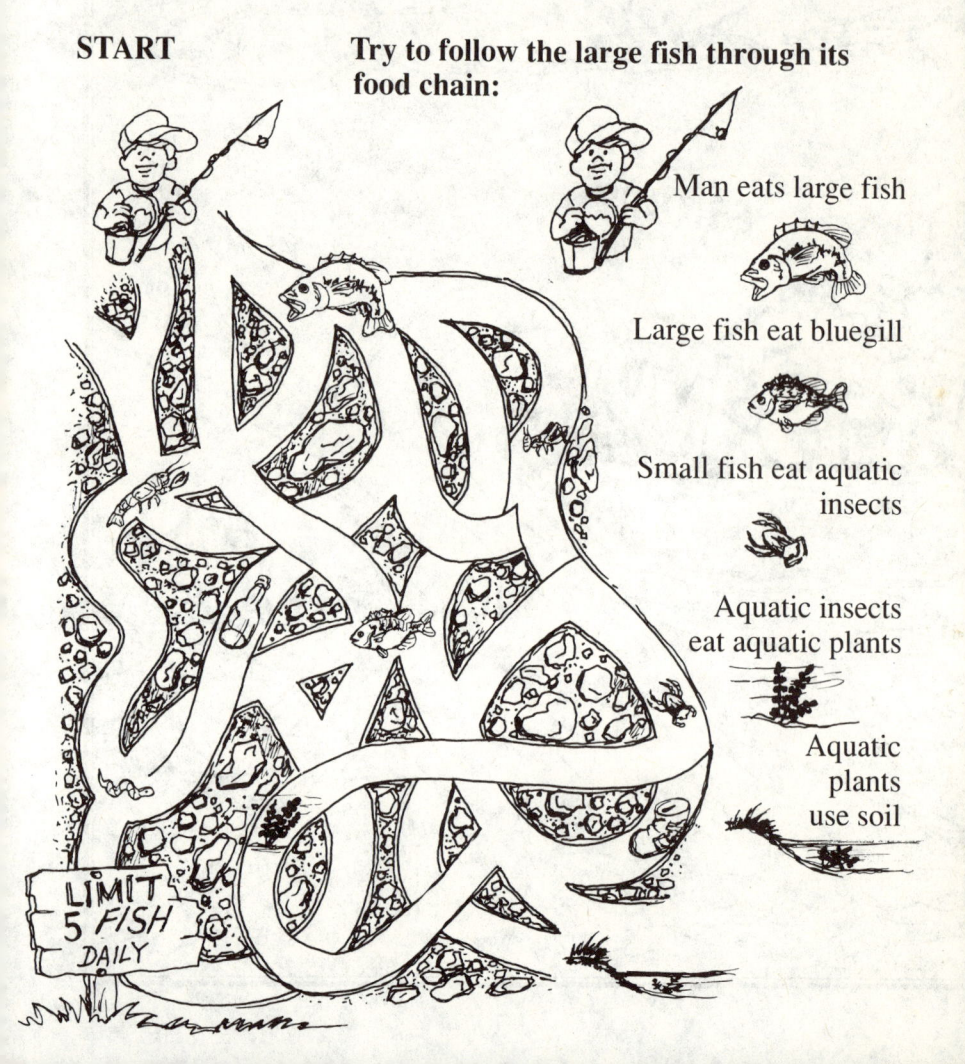

START

Try to follow the large fish through its food chain:

Man eats large fish

Large fish eat bluegill

Small fish eat aquatic insects

Aquatic insects eat aquatic plants

Aquatic plants use soil

LIMIT 5 FISH DAILY

Trashy Food

Some animals think litter is food, and they eat it. This makes them very sick or may even kill them.

Draw a line connecting the litter to the result it could have on an animal.

Answers: Broken bottles/jars to raccoon; Bottle caps to deer; Six-pack holder to duck; fishing line to heron.

A Fishy Crossword

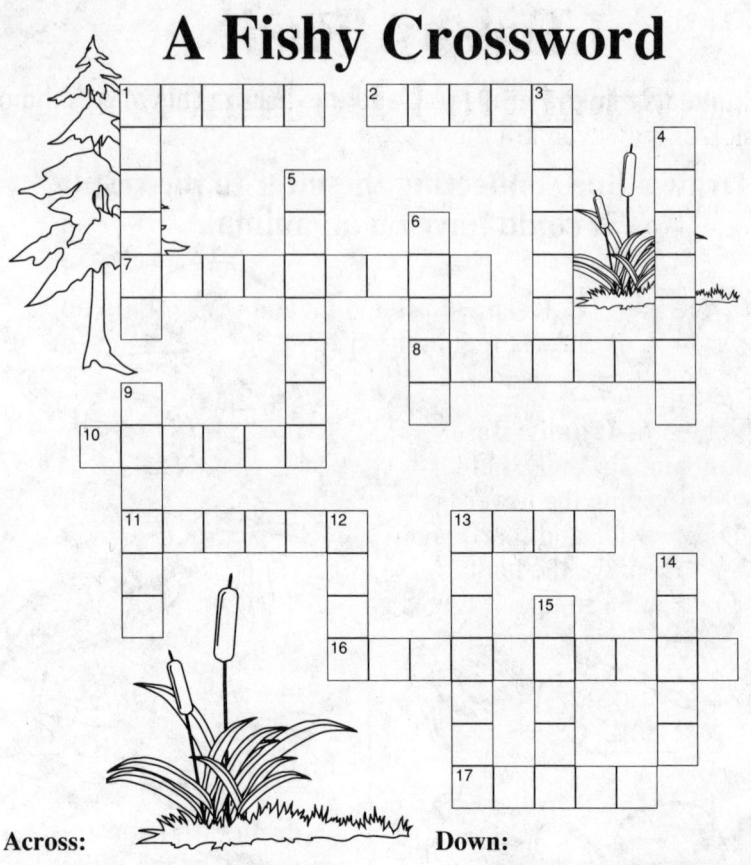

Across:

1. Fish in the ____. Fish cannot close their eyes, so they avoid light, bright water.
2. Fish use these to breathe.
7. This contains fishing equipment.
8. Crappie and Bass find these a filling meal.
10. Placed above the hook to show when a fish is nibbling or has been caught.
11. This is used to give your line weight for casting.
13. Fish like to ____ in a clean environment.
16. This must be worn when you are in a boat.
17. Artificial objects used to catch fish.

Down:

1. Remember, ____ first. Be careful around water & with hooks.
3. Protect your skin. Avoid ____.
4. This fish has whiskers.
5. A ____ knot will keep your hook on the line.
6. Catfish find these a tasty treat.
9. "Leaves of three ... Let it be," is the best way to know ____ Ivy.
12. Some people use a rod and ____ to fish with.
13. A ____ line helps a fish to hear.
14. Fish need ____ water to live in, polluted water can kill them.
15. Fish live in _____.

Answers: Across – 1. Shade 2. Gills 7. Tacklebox 8. Minnows 10. Bobber 11. Sinker 13. Live 16. Lifejacket 17. Lures   Down – 1. Safety 3. Sunburn 4. Catfish 5. Palomar 6. Worms 9. Poison 12. Reel 13. Lateral 14. Clean 15. Water

I Have A Fish! What Do I Do Now?

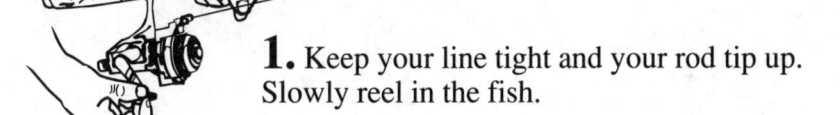

1. Keep your line tight and your rod tip up. Slowly reel in the fish.

2. Hold the fish firmly. Bass and most sunfish can be held easily by grasping the lower lip with thumb inside and forefinger outside. To remove the hook, push down and turn it so it comes out the way it went in.

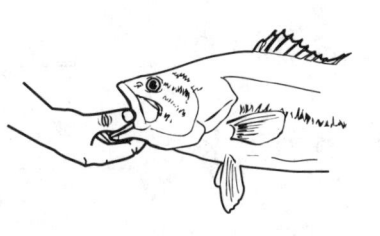

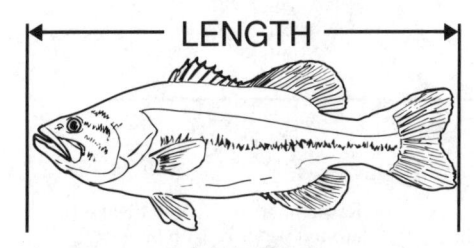

LENGTH

3. Is the fish large enough to keep? Will it be used for food? If not, carefully release the fish in the water. Handle the fish as little as possible and <u>do not put your fingers into the gills</u>. A fish that you catch and release carefully can be caught again someday when it is bigger.

4. You can keep many fish alive by threading a stringer under the chin and through the lower lip. Let the fish swim in the water. Tie the other end of the stringer tightly to the boat or bank. You can also use wire fish baskets to keep your fish alive.

Clean Water...
We Like Clean Water

Unscramble the letters to find out who we are. Use the pictures below as clues. Draw a line from the word to the picture it goes with.

1. h s i f __ __ __ __

2. a s l i n __ __ __ __ __

3. e n a k s __ __ __ __ __

4. g b s u __ __ __ __

5. l a p n s t __ __ __ __ __ __

Answers: fish, snail, snake, bugs, plants.

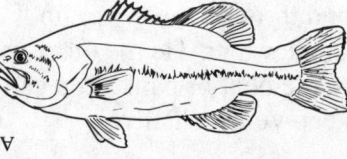

Water Babies

On the left side of this page are pictures of adult (grown up) animals and insects. On the right side of the page are their young, but the pictures are all mixed up! Can you match the young with their parents? Then color the pictures!

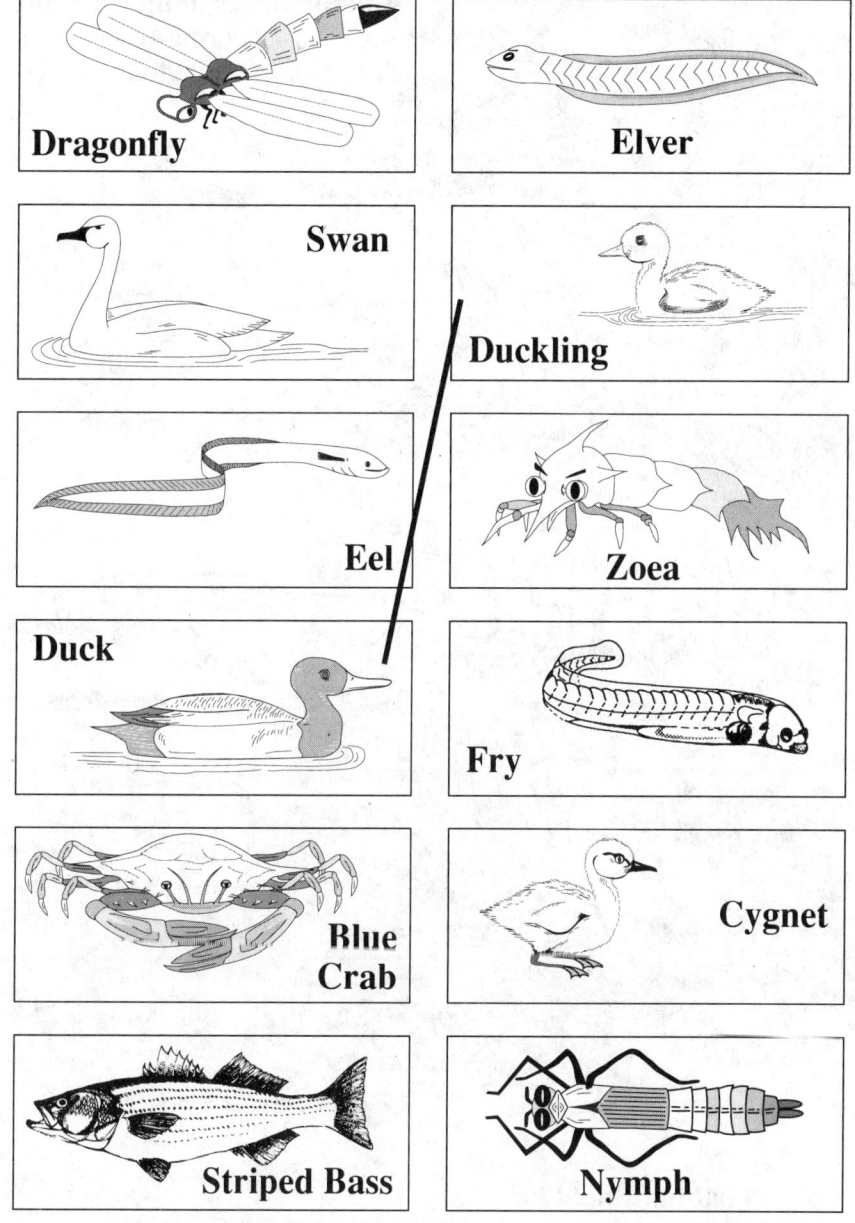

Dragonfly	Elver
Swan	Duckling
Eel	Zoea
Duck	Fry
Blue Crab	Cygnet
Striped Bass	Nymph

Answers: eel/elver; swan/cygnet; duck/duckling; dragonfly/nymph; striped bass/fry; blue crab/zoea

Which Habitat Would You Like To Visit?

A habitat is an animal's home and the surroundings from which its food comes.

Which habitat would have healthy animals around it?

Find The Source Of The Pollution

Clean water is very important. Start at the polluted water and go through the maze to find the cause of the pollution.

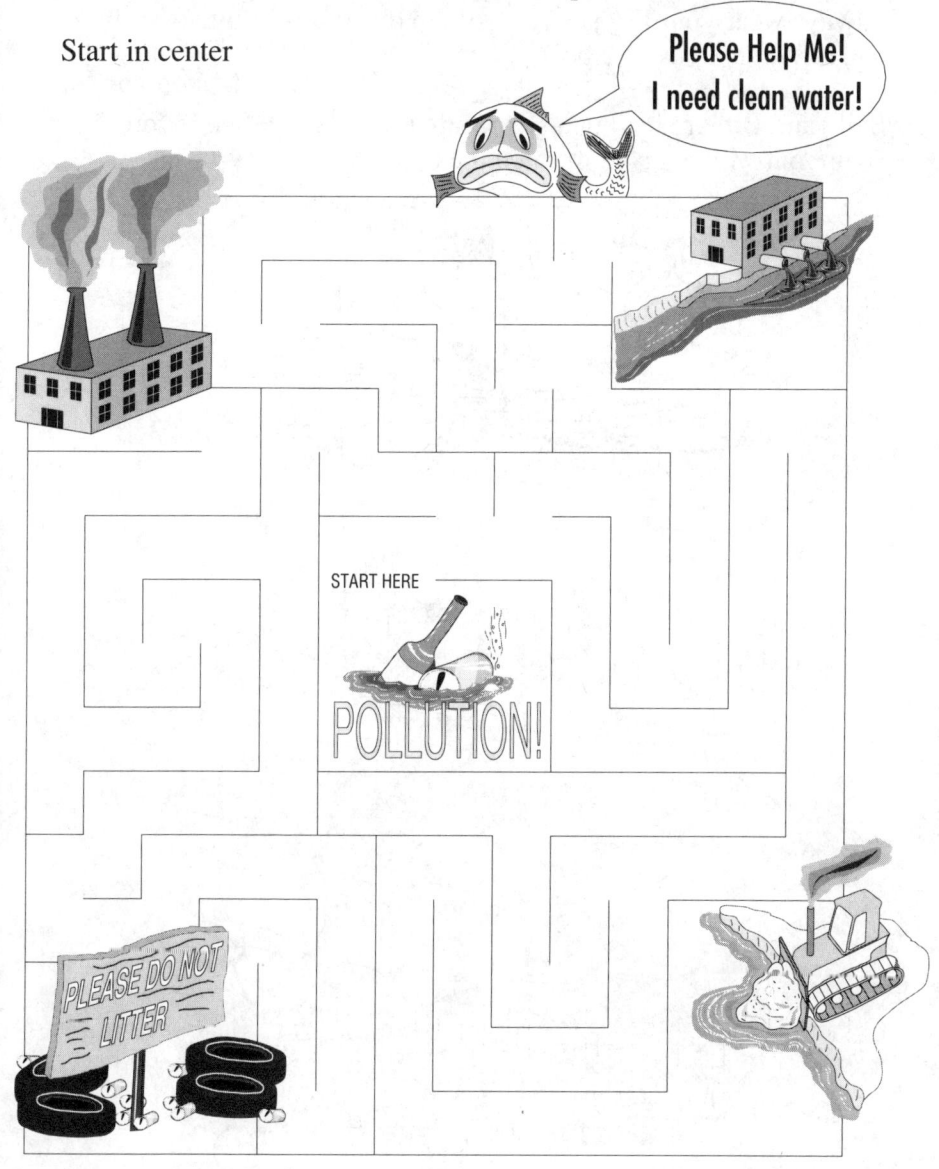

Start in center

Please Help Me! I need clean water!

START HERE

POLLUTION!

PLEASE DO NOT LITTER

Boating Safety Comes First!

Fishing and boating can be fun, but remember safety comes first!

Always wear your life jacket, don't go out in a boat by yourself, and never stand up in a boat.

Sally and Bill are having a good, safe time fishing. See if you can figure out who is about to catch the fish.

How Many Fish Can You Catch?

Players take turns connecting 2 dots. Lines go across or down, not diagonally. Complete as many small squares as you can. Initial each square you complete and take another turn. Squares in which fish are caught count 5 points. All other squares count 1 point.

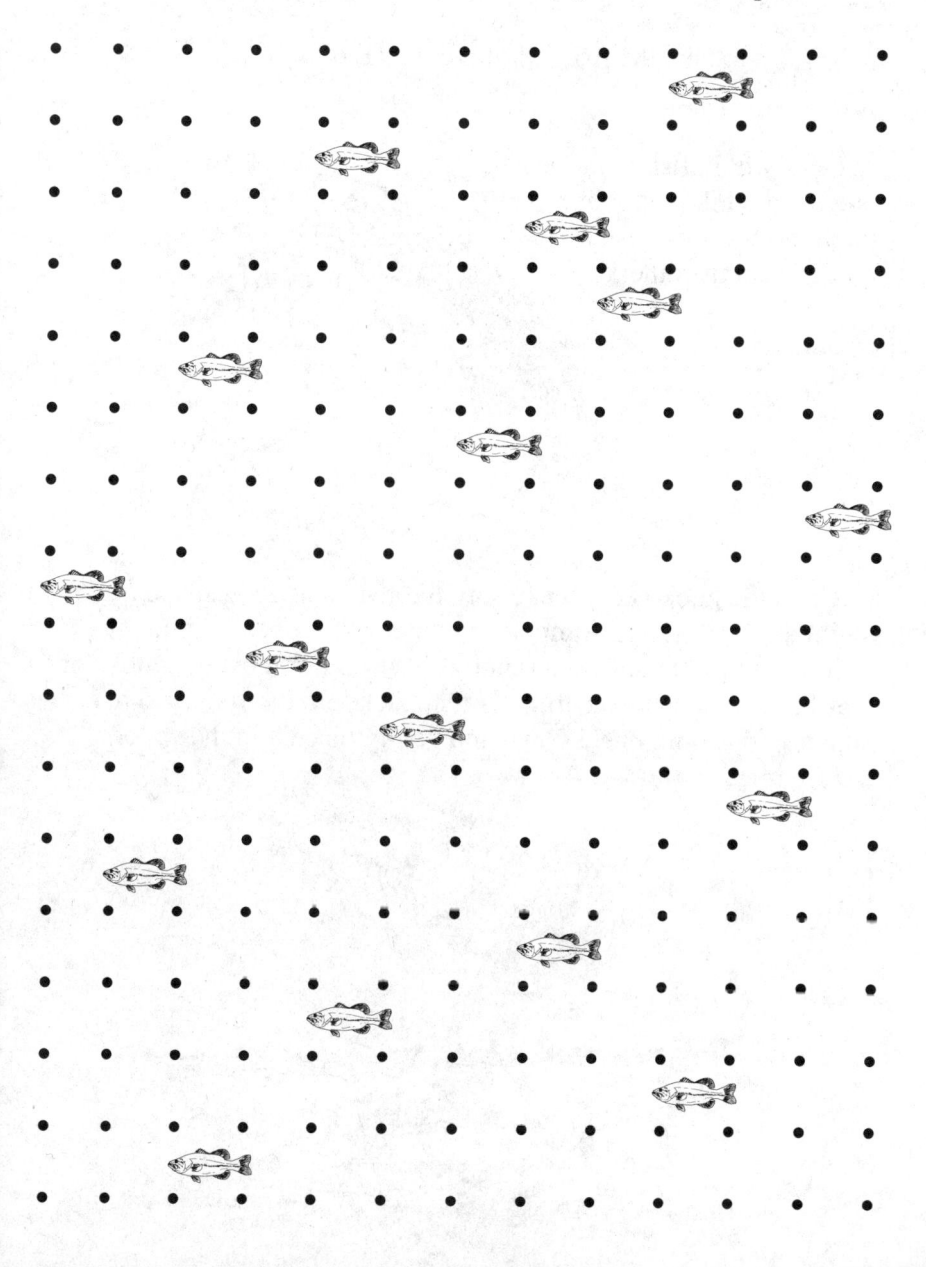

To Keep Or Not To Keep!

You don't have to keep all the fish you catch. You can release the ones you don't plan on eating.

To let a fish go:

1. Try not to take the fish out of the water, or

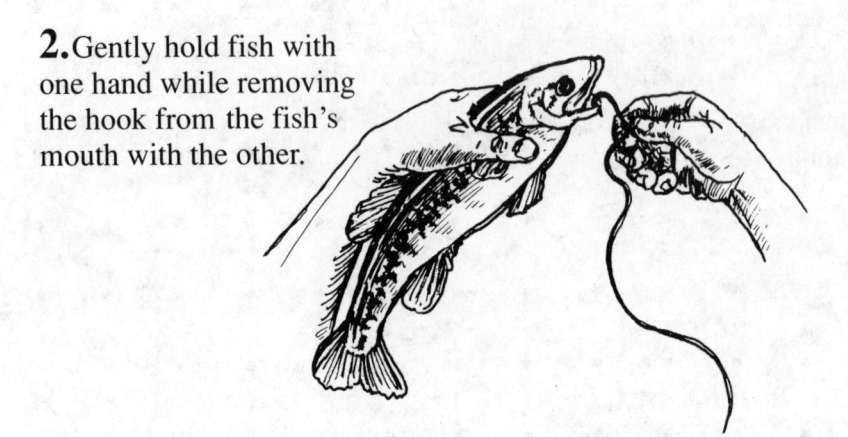

2. Gently hold fish with one hand while removing the hook from the fish's mouth with the other.

3. Once the hook is out make sure the fish is in good shape to swim away; if not, it is important to get water over the gills by holding it upright and face it into the current or move it gently forward in the lake. **Never** throw a fish back into the water from a standing position, kneel down and gently place it in the water before releasing it.

Water Home Search-A-Word

The following list is made up of the various animals that live near or in the water. Circle the words in the group of letters below.

- frogs
- birds
- turtles
- butterflies
- bees
- beaver
- ducks
- rabbits

- owl
- snakes
- crickets
- dragonfly
- ladybug
- fish
- lizard

- crawdads
- grasshopper
- raccoon
- amoeba
- paramecium
- worms
- salamander

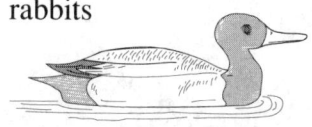

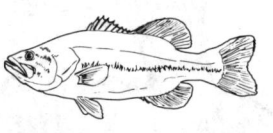

```
P A R R E P P O H S S A R G U B Y D A L D
A C C C R I C K E T S S T P L S M O R T R
R S R R O S C I C K E A T P D C K O H P A
A T U A F R O G S V W L P R W Y W S A B G
M O O W N A A B O E M A I A K O I R T S O
E C C D R C A D A T D B S C R F A W L A N
C F G A U C B Y B U T T E R F L I E S D F
I B I D S O H D U R C K S R A B B I A K L
U L E S B O E A V T E R D U C K S M L O Y
M D I A R N D S T L U R T L O Q S F A O P
A P S A V L A M A E N D E W R A B E M O D
R A M E C E I U M S T U L R T L E R A M A
A C A R G O R B E E E S T I B B A R N M D
M R W O R M S E E P P O H S S A R G D A A
E T H E M K B L I M L I Z A R D D R E E D
P A R A C O O N T O F I R E V O N U R R R
A R A S S N A K E S S E K A A M O E B A A
```

Fish Hide-N-Seek

The places where living things make their homes are called habitats. A fish's habitat can be in either salt water or fresh water. Saltwater habitats include bays and oceans. Habitat for freshwater fish are ponds, lakes, reservoirs, rivers, and streams.

Saltwater fish and freshwater fish like to hide and feed near underwater objects.

See if you can find the hiding fish. How many did you find?

Which Fish Will I Catch?

Unscramble the letters to find out the fish name. Match the fish name to the proper fish. Use the clues under each fish name to help you.

t f c i s a h

__ __ __ __ __ __ __ __

clue:
- has "whiskers"
- doesn't have scales
- has a deep forked tail
- likes to eat worms, liver and minnows

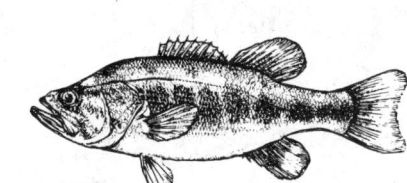

a l e r g   h o u m t   s a b s

__ __ __ __ __   __ __ __ __ __   __ __ __ __

clue:
- has a big mouth
- has dark strip or blotches down the side
- has two fins on back
- likes to eat minnows, crayfish and grasshoppers

h n s f u i s

__ __ __ __ __ __ __ __

clue:
- has dark ear flap
- flat body side to side
- small mouth
- likes to eat worms, crickets and grasshoppers

p c r a

__ __ __ __

clue:
- small turned down mouth
- large scales
- likes to eat worms, doughballs and corn

Answers: catfish, large mouth bass, sunfish, carp

Wetland Wonders

Wetlands are areas covered with plants that are wet for all or most of the year. Wetlands also are called marshes, swamps or bogs. They are very important habitat (home) to fish, ducks, frogs, turtles, salamanders and other very interesting wildlife.

In each group, circle the one animal or plant that does <u>not</u> belong in a wetland area.

1.
- Heron
- Dragonfly
- Turtle
- Mountain Lion

2.
- Fiddler Crab
- Jack Rabbit
- Muskrat
- Ducks

3.
- Camel
- Raccoon
- Marsh Hawk
- Shrimp

4.
- Bat
- Snake
- Minnows
- Bullfrog

Answers: 1. Mountain Lion 2. Jack Rabbit 3. Camel 4. Bat

We All Need A Clean Environment, Both People And Fish

Fish need clean water to live. Fish can't live in polluted water. Which things belong in the water? Draw a line from the pollution to the trash can. Circle the things that belong in the water.

Name These Fish!

Use the picture clues below to figure out the different types of fish. Add (+) or Subtract (-) letters according to the signs.

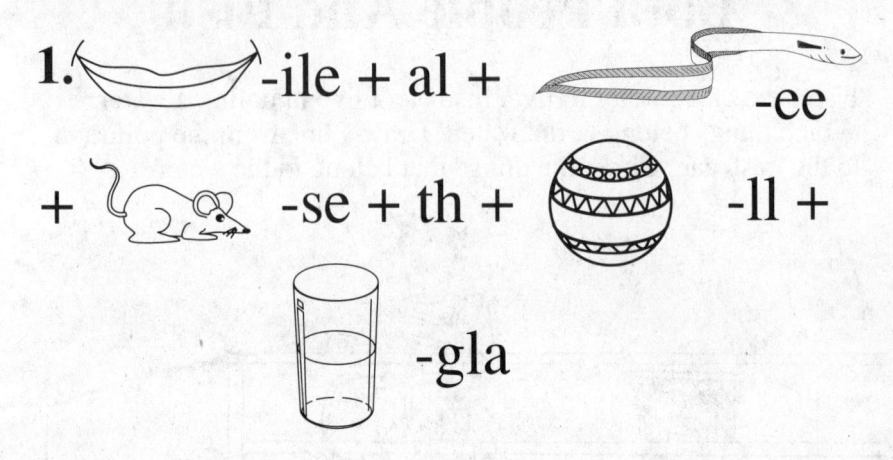

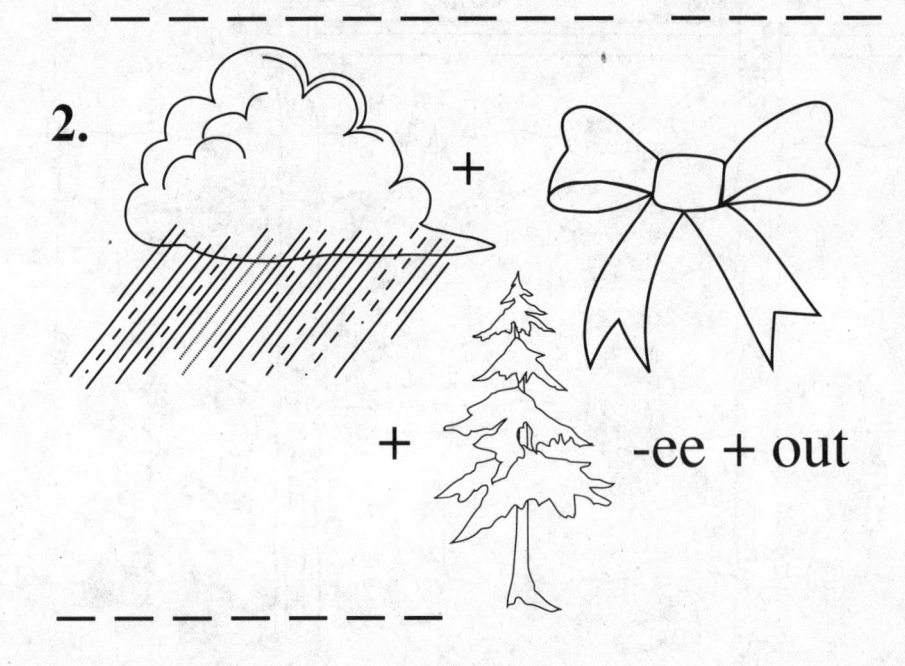

1. [bowl] -ile + al + [eel] -ee

   + [mouse] -se + th + [ball] -ll +

   [glass] -gla

   _ _ _ _ _ _ _ _ _ _

2. [cloud with rain] + [bow]

   + [tree] -ee + out

   _ _ _ _ _ _

   _ _ _ _ _

Answers: 1. Smallmouth Bass 2. Rainbow Trout